Autism Spectrum Disorder (ASD)

Autism Explained

Autism Types, Diagnosis, Symptoms, Treatment, Causes, Neurodevelopmental Disorders, Prognosis, Research, History, Myths, and More!

By Frederick Earlstein

Copyrights and Trademarks

Disclaimer and Legal Notice

Foreword

Autism has been described as a developmental disability that affects how certain people perceive the world and interact with others.

One of the most illuminating developments in our understanding of this condition is that it is not a "disease" that requires a "cure." Autism is simply a unique and different way of being in the world – one where autistic people often need to try a bit harder than others in order to function efficiently in the world and in their respective environments.

ASD has been defined as a "spectrum" and is now termed medically as Autism Spectrum Disorder (ASD). The use of the word "spectrum" highlights the many variables one finds in this condition – it has been said that no two people with autism are alike, and this has to do with their symptoms and the severity of their symptoms as much as with their adaptive abilities and unique individual characters.

Despite the often debilitating impairments of some of the symptoms of ASD, many autistic people nowadays find sufficient support in their environments to enable them to live productive and fulfilling lives. The first step, however, to a successful intervention and treatment is understanding and acceptance.

Table of Contents

Introduction

Autism – recently termed by the Diagnostic and Statistical Manual of Mental Disorders (DSM-5) as Autistic Spectrum Disorder (ASD), is an umbrella term encompassing several different types and classes of neurodevelopmental disorders characterized by impairments in social interaction, communication, and restricted and repetitive behavior. Nowadays, autism is used interchangeably with ASD.

This condition is diagnosed in a growing number of the population each year – 21.7 million people globally as of 2013, and 1 in every 68 people in the United States in 2014, with numbers projected to rise in the coming years.

Frustratingly, however, there is still much that we do not know about autism – for instance, its causes, and how it works – although recent studies have distinguished differences in brain development in persons with ASD, and identified a combination of both genetic and environmental factors as possible causes of the development of ASD.

It is a lifelong condition that starts early in a person's life – with symptoms changing as a person grows and matures. Despite our lack of knowledge and information regarding the mechanics of ASD, however, multiple disciplines have provided treatment options that have proven effective for several autistic persons in recent years. The first step towards effective treatment, however, is understanding and acceptance.

This book gathers numerous pertinent information and facts about ASD to help families and people better understand this condition, and in so doing, better support the growth and the development of their autistic child.

Important Terms to Know

Adaptive Skills – Self-help skills used for daily living

ABA – Applied Behavior Analysis

Allistic – Not autistic

Apraxia of speech – also verbal apraxia or dyspraxia, a speech disorder where a person has trouble saying what he or she wants to say correctly and consistently

ASD – Autism Spectrum Disorder

Asperger's Syndrome – A form of ASD characterized by normal IQ but impairments in social interaction and communication

At risk – Children vulnerable to developmental problems

Autism Spectrum Disorder – an umbrella term used to describe neurobiological disorders that affect a child's ability to interact, communicate, and learn. Also sometimes known as Pervasive Developmental Disorder (PDD)

Babbling – Vocalization that is precursor to real speech, typically begins at 6-9 months old

Childhood disintegrative disorder – an extremely rare pervasive developmental disorder in which a child appears to develop normally until the age of two, and then regresses

Cognitive – Cognition; mental processes including knowing, perceiving, remembering, judging, and reasoning

Compulsions – Deliberate, repetitive behaviors or actions with a set of rules for completion.

Developmental Delay – When a child is not functioning at an expected level for his/her age.

Developmental Disorder – Disorder that interrupts normal development in childhood, may affect a single or several areas of development

Developmental Milestones – Markers of ability used to monitor a child's development, including skills and behaviors that develop at a certain age

DSM – Diagnostic and Statistical Manual of Mental Disorders, the official manual of the American Psychiatric Association

Disability – Physical or mental condition that can lead to developmental delay

Early Intervention – support system and coordinated services designed to promote a child's developmental growth and the ability to cope with disabilities

Echolalia – Repetition of words, phrases, intonation, or sounds of others.

Epidemiology – study of how often diseases occur in different groups and why

Epilepsy – Brain disorder involving recurrent seizures

Executive Function – Cognitive process that regulates a person's ability to organize thoughts and activities, prioritize tasks, manage time efficiently, and make decisions

Eye Gaze – nonverbal form of communication signaling interest in interacting

Functional Play – The appropriate use of objects in play

High functioning autism – Autism in individuals with normal/near-normal IQ

Hyperresponsiveness – Abnormal sensitivity to sensory input

Hyporesponsiveness – Abnormal insensitivity to sensory input

Neurological – having to do with the nerves or the nervous system

Neurotransmitter – Chemical messenger released from one nerve cell which makes its way to another nerve cell, influencing a particular chemical reaction to occur

OCD – Obsessive Compulsive Disorder

PDD – Pervasive Developmental Disorders

Repetitive Motor Mannerisms – Repetition of movements or posturing of the body

Restricted patterns of interest – limited range of interests that are intense in focus

Rett's Disorder – Rare genetic disorder in females, where a child appears to develop normally for a period then regresses

Rituals – Repeated behaviors that appear to be meaningless but are repeated in certain situations or circumstances

Selective Serotonin Reuptake Inhibitors – Class of antidepressant medicine

Sensory Input – Internal and external sensations

Sensory Stimulation – Behaviors performed to stimulate internal response

Special Needs – A child with a mental or physical disability that requires special services or treatment.

Stereotyped Behaviors – Abnormal or excessive repetition of actions

Stimming – Self-Stimulating behaviors

Tactile Defensiveness – A strong, negative response to sensations like touch

Tic – Repetitive movement that is difficult, if not impossible, to control

Tantrum – Expression of intense frustration, typical of children who cannot express emotions or verbalize their needs

Chapter One: What is Autism?

The word "autism" was first used by Swiss psychiatrist Eugen Bleuler in 1910. His terminology was more appropriately the New Latin word "autismus" – derived from Greek "autos" which meant "self." The English translation of "autismus" is "autism." At the time, however, Bleuler was defining not autism as we now know it per se, but merely certain symptoms of schizophrenia. For a long time, in fact, schizophrenia and autism were integrally linked in the minds of many researchers and medical scientists.

Nowadays, autism is considered a distinct neurodevelopmental disorder. The essential use of the Greek term "self" does seem incisive in describing some of the behavioral symptoms that characterize this condition: impaired social interaction, verbal and nonverbal communication, and an obsessive, repetitive behavior which considers "outside influence to be an intolerable disturbance." But what seems strange behavior to other people is also true in the reverse – that is, to individuals with autism, the world, and other people, may also seem strange and oftentimes overwhelming, and this can cause them considerable confusion and anxiety.

This is a lifelong condition, but depending on the severity of the symptoms and the effectiveness of treatments, some may still be able to lead relatively normal lives. Studies support the theory that early intervention makes a significant difference in helping the person with autism cope with their condition. That is why early diagnosis is important.

This chapter covers some of the basics regarding autism: its definition, a brief history, and the myths and misconceptions that have dogged autism since it was first observed in the early 1700s.

Defining Autism

Under the Individuals with Disabilities Education Act (IDEA), autism is defined as "a developmental disability significantly affecting verbal and nonverbal communication and social interaction, generally evident before age three, that adversely affects a child's educational performance." It is characterized by:

- Engaging in repetitive activities and stereotyped movements,

- Resistance to environmental change or change in daily routines, and

- Unusual responses to sensory experiences

This is a lifelong developmental condition affecting the way a person relates to his environment and to other people. The important thing to remember is that autism is not an illness or disease – it is a condition which affects the way people perceive the world, how they interact with others, and how they learn and develop. It is not something that can be "cured," but it is a condition which necessitates a different kind of support and lifestyle in order to help people with autism to live more fulfilling lives. This is important because the difficulty they have in communicating – expressing themselves and understanding what other people think and feel, makes it doubly more difficult for people with autism to function in the world and to make themselves understood.

In 2014, the Diagnostic and Statistical Manual of Mental Disorders (DSM) 5 by the American Psychiatric Association (APA) has changed the general term of Autism to Autism Spectrum Disorder (ASD). It is now considered an umbrella term encompassing disorders that were once considered separate such as autistic disorder, Asperger's syndrome, childhood disintegrative disorder, and pervasive developmental disorder-not otherwise specific (PDD-NOS). The use of the word spectrum means that it covers a wide range of difficulties – more severe for some than for others - in social communication, social interaction, and restricted or repetitive behaviors and interests. No two people with autism will have exactly the same symptoms, although in general, a person with ASD will prefer to stick to a set of behaviors and will resist both major and minor changes to their daily activities.

In recent years, the number of children diagnosed with ASD has risen, but it is not year clear whether this is due to a real increase in numbers, or because of better detection and reporting of individual cases.

Myths about Autism Spectrum Disorder

One of the major difficulties that people with autism have is the lack of understanding that other people have of their condition. Myths and misconceptions, and even some very unfair judgments, have been made about autistic people , and their families, for years. This lack of reliable information not only makes it more difficult for autistic people to be understood, it also makes their access to reliable support systems difficult. Perhaps one of the more troubling realities is how much many of these misconceptions persist to this day.

The following are some of the myths and misconceptions about autism that still persist among people today:

- *That vaccines cause autism.* There is simply no direct evidence to back up the claim that childhood vaccines cause autism. A previous study to this effect done in 1998 has since been retracted.
- *That autism is caused by "refrigerator mothers."* The precise cause of autism has not yet been determined, but it is now widely accepted that parenting styles have nothing whatsoever to do with the development of autism.
- *That autism is caused solely by environmental factors.* While environmental factors can certainly contribute to the severity of the symptoms of autism in certain individuals, these are not the sole cause. Genetic factors have been identified as one of the causes of autism – and one child diagnosed with autism increases the chances that the rest of the siblings may also have autism.
- *That autism is a mental health disorder.* Autism is actually a neurological disorder, which means that autism is characterized by abnormalities in brain structure and neurotransmitter levels. Some people with autism – though not all, do have co-occurring mental health disorders that will also require treatment.

- *That all individuals with autism have mental disabilities.* Individuals with autism have a very wide range of intellectual abilities – the difficulty is that it is very difficult to test the intelligence of those with autism due to their differing language and interpersonal skills and analysis. But plenty of people with autism have even earned college degrees and held regular jobs in a variety of professions.

- *That individuals with autism are violent and a danger to society.* Most instances of violent or aggressive behavior on the part of individuals with autism are usually prompted by sensory overload or emotional distress, hardly ever is it due to malice. Individuals with autism don't really pose a danger to society – in fact, they often prefer to limit their exposure to society because of the anxiety this can provoke in them.

- *That children with autism are unruly or spoiled and simply need to be disciplined.* Traditional methods of discipline simply will not work on children with autism. Most of what may be perceived as tantrums or bad behavior may actually stem from the difficulties they face given their unique symptoms – such as sensory overload, or the frustration of trying but not being able to communicate effectively with others. Parents must be able to distinguish between the times when their child is behaving badly, and when it they are simply experiencing unique communication or social difficulties. Obviously, each behavioral type must be dealt with appropriately.

- *That individuals with autism do not talk.* Many individuals with autism can develop a good functional language, and most others develop functional means of communication through the use of computers, sign language, electronic devices, or the use of pictures.

- *That individuals with autism are savants.* Only about 10 percent of individuals with autism exhibit savant abilities. Some have above-average performance abilities in only one or two areas, and these are referred to as "splinter skills." The uneven nature or development of their skills may lead some to think that within each child with autism lies a genius, but there are some that exhibit above normal intelligence just as there are also some that exhibit very low intellectual functioning. The truth is that it is just very difficult to measure the intellectual capabilities of individuals with autism, and children with splendid skills in a few areas may also exhibit significant delay in certain other areas of mental processing.

- *That individuals with autism are unable or unwilling to form meaningful social relationships.* People with autism can have greater difficulty in social interactions, but this does not mean that they do not or cannot feel loving emotions for other people – even though they may express it differently or in less obvious and less conventional ways. Some who have autism have been able to form close relationships, have friends, even fallen in love and raised children. Despite their "aloofness," people with autism can have a great capacity for emotional connection – and sometimes all it requires is a willingness to give and accept love on their terms.

- *Individuals with autism do not like being touched.* This can be true for some, but not for everyone with autism. The avoidance of physical contact is usually due to high sensory sensitivities, but many with autism actually enjoy hugs and other forms of touch.

- *Individuals with autism have no sense of humor.* Again, while this may be true for some, it is not true for all people with autism. Many express humor in their unique ways, and they can tease, tell jokes, or even mimic comic lines or actions in an attempt to entertain others.

- *That children with autism can't learn.* Having autism does not negate one's capacity for learning or intellectual processing. All it means that learning has to be tailored to the specific needs of each child. Progress might be slow, but as long as family and teachers are patient and persistent, and the appropriate and effective teaching methods are used, learning can proceed slowly but steadily.

- *That autism can be "outgrown."* Autism is a lifelong condition, and there is no cure for it, just as one does not outgrow it. What individuals with autism can do is learn to cope with their symptoms and with enough progress, still be able to live a functional and meaningful life as much as possible. The people around them can also help them best by accepting their unique nature, while also providing a solid social and support structure.

History of Autism Spectrum Disorder (ASD)

Autism is not a new medical condition – though our understanding of it has certainly changed dramatically over the years. Largely because of the vivid behavioral characteristics that define the symptoms of autism, this condition has been rife with misconceptions, speculation, and even superstition. It was said that Martin Luther once considered a severely autistic 12-year old boy as possessed. On the other hand, a feral child caught in 1798 who showed signs of autism was the subject of the book "The Wild Boy of Aveyron." The book went on to describe how Jean Itard attempted to treat him through a behavioral program to help him form social attachments and induce speech via imitation.

The specific word "autism" was first used by Eugen Bleuler, a Swiss psychiatrist, sometime in 1911. The word itself derives from the Greek word "autos" which means "self," and is used to describe the essential characteristic of persons with autism who seem isolated in themselves – i.e, removed from social interaction. Originally, however, autism was not regarded as a distinct condition, but merely as one group of schizophrenic symptoms. Autism was then used to describe schizophrenic patients who were especially withdrawn and self-absorbed. This link between autism and schizophrenia was dominant among many researchers' minds until the 1960s. Only afterwards did medical professionals begin to consider autism in children as distinct and separate from schizophrenia.

Prior to this time, during the 1940s, researchers in the United States started to use the term "autism" to describe children with emotional or social problems. In 1943, at John Hopkins University, Dr. Leo Kanner used the term to describe the withdrawn behavior of several children. In describing 11 children who were highly intelligent but who displayed a powerful desire for aloneness and an obsessive insistence on persistent sameness, he used the term "early infantile autism."

At about the same time, in Germany, scientist Hans Asperger also identified a similar condition, which is now referred to as Asperger's syndrome. This was a "milder" form of autism, and mainly centered around highly intelligent boys who had trouble with social interactions and who also had specific obsessive interests.

Autism as was understood at that time was rife with many misconceptions and false theories. One example is the theory of "refrigerator mothers" or frigid mothers popularized by psychologist Bruno Bettelheim. According to him, autism was caused by mothers not loving their children enough – a theory that was ultimately debunked by a 1977 research on twins that found the cause of autism as largely being genetic and due to biological differences in brain development. The first solid argument against the refrigerator mother theory, however, was formulated by Bernard Rimland in 1964. He was the father of a son with autism, and he was the first who argued that autism was not caused by the parent-child bond but was actually a biological condition. Unfortunately, by the beginning of the 1980s, many parents still confused autism with mental retardation and psychosis.

Such myths and misconceptions were also prevalent in the treatment methods for autism. From the 1960s to the 1970s, autism treatments focused more on medication such as LSD, electric shock, and behavioral change techniques which relied on pain and punishment.

Thankfully, as our understanding of this condition grew, so did our attempts at prescribing more humane treatments. In 1980, "Infantile Autism" was listed in the Diagnostic and

Statistical manual of Mental Disorders (DSM) for the first time, and was finally officially separated from childhood schizophrenia. From then on, the terms evolved. In 1987, infantile autism was replaced with "autism disorder," along with a study regarding the potential use of behavior therapy as treatment. During the 1980s and the 1990s, behavioral therapy and highly controlled learning environments became the primary treatments for autism. The cornerstone of autism therapy at present are behavioral therapy and language therapy, with other treatments being added as needed.

In 1991, autism was made a special education category by the federal government, and children with autism were offered special educational services. Subsequently, in 1944, Asperger's Syndrome was also added to DSM, thereby expanding the scope and coverage of the autism spectrum as including milder cases of autism even among individuals who could still function socially.

In 2014, DSM-5 incorporated all subcategories into one umbrella diagnosis which they referred to as Autism Spectrum Disorder (ASD).

Chapter Two: Types of Autism

In the more recent DSM-5 (2013), the APA eliminated the different subtypes of autism listed in the DSM fourth edition. The different subtypes were dissolved into one diagnosis that is now called Autism Spectrum Disorder (ASD), which is now used interchangeably with autism.

This was supposed to represent an effort for a more accurate diagnosis of individuals who showed signs of autism.

It remains to be seen how this change will affect how autism will be treated by specialists. To this day, many clinicians, parents, therapists, and organizations still do continue to use the terms and distinctions provided under the different subtypes of autism that was set out in the DSM fourth edition.

The CDC still classifies three main types of ASD, which are:

- Autistic Disorder

- Asperger's Syndrome

- Pervasive Developmental Disorder, not otherwise specified (PDD-NOS)

In addition, DSM-IV also provided two rare but severe autistic-like conditions:

- Rett Syndrome

- Childhood Disintegrative Disorder

In this chapter, we take a closer look at these five different identified subtypes of autism, keeping in mind the recent move towards the integration of these different subtypes into the singular term "Autism Spectrum Disorders" (ASD).

Types of Autism

Autistic Disorder

Sometimes also called "Classic" Autism, Autistic Disorder is usually what comes to mind when people think of the word autism. It is also what is referred to when the terms childhood autism, early infantile autism, and Kanner's syndrome or infantile psychosis, are used. Individuals with Autistic Disorder typically manifest language delays, social and communication challenges, and unusual behaviors and interests.

The impairments of those suffering from autistic disorder are comparatively more severe, and involve impairments in social and language functioning, repetitive behavior, and may also include mental retardation and seizures.

Asperger's Syndrome

People with Asperger's Syndrom typically only have milder symptoms of autism. That is, despite social challenges, unusual behaviors and interests, they generally do not have problems with language or intellectual disability. In fact, they generally tend to score in the average or above average range in intelligence tests. This tends to affect boys more than girls, and is characterized by an obsessive interest in a single object or topic, which they can research and discuss nonstop. General social skills, however, are markedly impaired. As they enter adulthood, they are at a greater risk for developing anxiety and depression.

Asperger's Syndrome was removed from the diagnostic manual in 2013, but people still continue to use it because of its usefulness in describing a very specific group of people – even with a tough time in social communication, their above average intelligence makes individuals with Asperger's Syndrome seem "quirky"- prompting the more common terms "geek syndrome" or "little professor syndrome." Some doctors also refer to this syndrome as "high-functioning autism (HFA)."

Pervasive Developmental Disorder, not otherwise specified (PDD-NOS)

Also called "Atypical Autism," PDD-NOS is usually the diagnosis for people who meet some, but not all, of the criteria for Autistic Disorder or Asperger Syndrome. Usually, the symptoms are milder compared to Autistic

Disorder though more severe than Asperger's Syndrome, and usually involve social and communication challenges. The age of onset is also usually later compared to the other types. PDD-NOS is kind of a catch-all category for children manifesting autistic behaviors but who do not fit into the other categories. The symptoms can range from very mild to very severe. With the removal of PDD-NOS as a subtype from DSM-5, the newer diagnosis "Social Communication Disorder" may serve the same function of being a catch-all category.

Rett Syndrome

This is no longer considered to be a subtype of autism, although those with Rett syndrome may still display autism-like symptoms. When this happens, then they have both Rett Syndrom as well as ASD.

This is a rare genetic condition that affects only girls, and was the only one in the former subtypes that could be diagnosed medically. This is caused by a genetic mutation and apparently only occurs randomly, rather than being inherited. It is characterized by severe symptoms such as social communication challenges, as well as a severe impairment of a girl's ability to use her hands. From 6 to 18 months of age, the child begins to stop responding socially, habitually wrings her hands, and loses language skills.

Coordination problems appear and can become severe. By the age of two, head growth falls far below normal.

Childhood Disintegrative Disorder (CDD)

In CDD, children develop normally for the first two years and then lose some or most of their communication and social skills. This disorder is extremely rare, however, and its existence as a separate condition is still being debated.

This is a very rare disorder affecting boys more often than girls, and it is also the most severe in the autistic spectrum disorder. After a period of normal development from 2 to 4 years of age, a child begins to rapidly lose multiple areas of function, including social and language skills and intellectual abilities. The child may also often develop a seizure disorder. This can become a severe impairment, and lost functions are no longer recovered.

Chapter Three: Causes of Autism

The state of knowledge regarding the cause or causes of autism is still, unfortunately, incomplete. While genetic factors do seem to predominate, the complexity of autism as a disorder has led to an increasing suspicion among experts that there may not be a single, common cause, but rather a set of core aspects with distinct causes. And because autism as it is now defined covers a broad spectrum of related disorders, each covering different underlying brain dysfunctions, and resulting in no two persons having the same symptoms or type of autism, a multiplicity of causes does seem more plausible rather than a singular cause that unites all the different types and manifestations of autism.

Current research suggests that both genetics and environmental aspects play a role, with genetic factors predominating. The dearth of knowledge regarding the causation of autism has led people to wild, and often weird, ideas about environmental factors that may possibly cause autism – from vaccines, watching too much television, parental coldness towards their children, and even sex positions during conception. In this chapter, we take a look at both the genetic and environmental factors that may affect brain development and thereby cause autism – while sticking as close as possible to verifiable data rather than speculation and suppositions.

1. Genetic Factors

While a specific gene linked to ASD has yet to be identified, studies have shown that younger siblings of children with ASD have a 5-20% chance of also developing the condition – also called "recurrence risk." There is also a 50-80% greater likelihood for identical twins to develop ASD (5-20% chance for fraternal twins). There is also a greater likelihood that parents or other relatives will also have some form of mild social impairment that is very similar to some of the many symptoms of autism. This pattern of autism or autism-related disabilities running in families support the theory of a genetic basis for the condition.

Several candidates have been looked at – including single gene mutations and chromosomal abnormalities. The difficulty is that not one of them is sufficient to explain large numbers of cases of autism. Individually, each seem able to explain only less than 1% of autism cases. More than 100 autism-risk genes have been identified so far, but the difficulty is that even when these genes are identified, autism still seems to be tied to a complex interaction of genetic risks and environmental factors that influence early development. Neither genetics nor environmental factors, however, actually *cause* autism. The presence of genetic factors, however, when other environmental factors are also present, does seem to increase the risk of a child developing autism.

Another theory is that synaptic dysfunction may cause autism. Based on gene replacement studies in mice, autistic symptoms seem to arise from developmental steps and stages that occur during the first eight weeks from conception – and these are dependent on synaptic activity. Of course, this does not preclude the possibility that autism may still begin at a later stage, or after eight weeks.

2. Environmental Factors

It must be stressed again that our knowledge of the precise cause or causes of autism is still insufficient, and just as there are no specific genetic factors that can be isolated as a causative factor, neither have there been any definite evidence that environmental factors, whether alone or in combination with others, can cause ASD. At most, what can probably be said is that external factors might trigger ASD in children who are already genetically prone to developing the condition, or that in combination with genetic risk factors, environmental factors modestly increase the risk of the development of autism.

Prenatal Environment

It must be stated again that there is no single environmental cause that has been isolated as a definite cause of autism, but links between certain environmental factors and autism have been established through epidemiological studies – or the study of patterns of health and disease conditions in defined populations. Several of these environmental factors are those which have been identified as being present during prenatal life.

Bacterial or viral infections

There seems to be a slight increase in the risk of autism when the mother suffers from bacterial or viral infections during pregnancy. This can be due to either the harmful infectious organisms passing from the mother to the fetus through the placenta, or because the mother's immune response to the bacteria is detrimental to the developing brain of the fetus. Prenatal viral infection is considered the principal non-genetic cause of autism, particularly maternal exposure to the cytomegalovirus and the rubella virus (German Measles or Three-Day Measles). The development of congenital rubella syndrome (CRS) in a child as a result of infection during early pregnancy has been considered the most convincing environmental cause for autism.

Thyroxine deficiency

Thyroid problems that lead to thyroxine deficiency during the 8th-12th weeks of pregnancy may also lead to changes in the fetal brain that can also lead to autism. Thyroxine deficiency can be caused by inadequate iodine in one's diet, and environmental agents that can interfere with iodine uptake such as flavonoids, tobacco smoke, and herbicides.

Folic acid deficiency

While studies regarding folic acid deficiency do not support a finding of causality with autism, it has been reasonably established that the use of folic acid supplementation around the time of conception reduces the risk of neural tube defects in children. There is also evidence that the use of maternal folic acid supplements during pregnancy is associated with a reduced risk of neurodevelopmental disorders in children. Today, there is a widespread general recommendation for women planning to become pregnant to take a daily supplement of folic acid starting one month before conception. Studies show that maternal use of supplemental folic acid from 4 weeks prior to until 8 weeks after the start of pregnancy resulted in a lower risk of autistic disorder – what is considered the most severe form of ASD – in children. Multiple studies support the hypothesis that taking folic acid during pregnancy could significantly reduce cases of autism by modulating gene expression through an epigenetic mechanism.

More than 50 countries in the world today require fortification of certain foods with folic acid to decrease the rate of NTDs in the population.

Gestational or maternal diabetes

Gestational diabetes or diabetes in the mother during pregnancy is considered a significant risk factor for autism – up to a twofold increased risk.

The presence of GDM diagnosed 26 weeks or earlier during pregnancy seems to contribute to a higher risk that a child may develop ASD.

Use of certain antidepressants

Studies seem to show that prenatal exposure to Selective Serotonin Reuptake Inhibitors (SSRI) as treatment for depression may increase susceptibility to ASD in boys, though it is still not clear whether there is any causal link between these two variables. On the other hand, the use of prenatal SSRI should also be balanced with the possible effects of untreated maternal depression for the child.

Being an older parent/older father

Studies have also shown that fathers over the age of 50 have a greater chance of passing on de novo mutations, and therefore also run a greater risk of having a child with ASD. Being of advanced parental age for both the father and mother may also increase the risk for ASD.

Prenatal Stress

Prenatal stress that can span anything from significant life events to environmental factors, causing distress in an expectant mother, may also contribute to the development of autism – though as part of a gene-environment interaction rather than as a causative factor in itself. Stressors can include job loss, family discord, and environmental factors such as prenatal exposure to storms. Such events may disrupt brain development and produce behaviors resembling autism symptoms.

Fetal testosterone theory

According to this theory, high levels of testosterone in the amniotic fluid can push the brain to develop in terms of the ability to see and analyze complex patterns and systems, while at the same time diminishing the development of communication and empathetic skills. "Male" traits are emphasized over "female" traits, thus producing behaviors similar to certain symptoms of autism.

Perinatal Environment

Certain perinatal and obstetric environments have also been identified as possible risk factors for the development of autism, including:

- Low birth weight

- Gestation duration and premature birth (or before 35 weeks)

- Hypoxia during childbirth

- Exposure to air pollution

- Other difficulties during birth that may involve periods of oxygen deprivation to the baby's brain

Postnatal Environment

There have also been a number of postnatal environmental factors that have been proposed as causal agents or triggers in the development of autism. Many of these have, in fact, taken people's imagination by storm. But the truth is that there is simply no reliable study or evidence to show that any factors taking place after birth, or that a child's exposure to environmental factors after they are born, increases the risk of ASD.

Just some of these hypothesized causes of autism that have not been proven or confirmed by any evidence whatsoever include:

- Vaccines, including the MMR vaccine, and the mercury-based Thiomersal

- The way a person has been brought up, or refrigerator mothers

- Diet, such as eating gluten or dairy products

- Autoimmune disease

- Exposure to opiates

- Gastrointestinal problems in the child

- Lack of vitamin D

- Lead poisoning

- Mercury poisoning

- Viral infection

Chapter Four: Brain Development and ASD

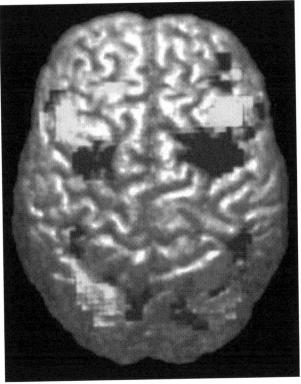

For years, autism has been defined by three behavioral hallmarks: impaired social interaction, communication difficulties, and repetitive behaviors. A specific cause or causes of autism has yet to be identified, and *how* autism works has yet to be fully understood. It has been proposed that autistic behaviors are adaptive responses based on differences in the early development of brain structure and function.

New studies have yielded new theories regarding the pathology of brain growth and development among children with autism. Using Magnetic Resonance Imaging (MRI), researchers have found that autism is characterized by certain differences in early brain growth and structure as opposed to the typical brain development in children.

But while these brain characteristics have been observed in individuals with autism, a clear and unifying brain difference has yet to be found that is shared by different individuals diagnosed with autism. The difficulty lies in the natural complexity of how the brain works, and the unlikelihood that autism affects just one area of the brain alone. Autism affects an individual's cognitive, language, and sensory abilities, thus making it likely that more than one brain region is affected. Nevertheless, just as the possible causes of autism have been identified as early as during a baby's prenatal and perinatal development, it is possible that autism is linked to differences in prenatal brain development. In other words, the differences in brain development of individuals with autism may begin as early as prenatal or fetal life, or soon after conception.

Brain Overgrowth followed by Premature Arrest of Growth

For years, "brain overgrowth" during early development was considered as a risk factor for a later diagnosis of autism. It is still unclear, however, how the differences in size or patterns of growth in the different brain regions affect or lead to autistic behaviors. "Brain overgrowth" refers to a tendency of the brain to grow too fast during early childhood, especially during the first three years of life.

UCLA researchers have also found that brain development in regions responsible for language and social skills grow more slowly in boys with autism than in children that do not have autism. The brain growth among individuals with autism seems characterized by three phases:

1. Early brain overgrowth;

2. A slowing or arrest of growth during early childhood; and

3. Possible degeneration by preadolescence, and continuing well into adulthood.

This delay in brain development during the struggle to develop social interactions, refine emotional skills, and the establishment of a personal identity during the critical period of adolescence could explain much of the struggles of individuals with autism. Brain imaging scans showed a slower development of the white matter connections in the regions of the brain that are important to language and social skills, what researchers have referred to as white matter impairment. On the other hand, learning, cognitive and emotional processing – and the cells and connections responsible for these – were never properly pruned away.

The result is an unusual brain circuitry in which cells are overly connected to their closer neighbors, and under-connected to more distant but nevertheless important cells in the brain. As a result, it is more difficult for the brain to process information "normally." What is still not clear, however, is why the brain develops differently in individuals with autism.

Brain Connectivity

Brain connectivity relates to how well and how effectively two areas of the brain communicate with each other. A distinction is made between short-range connections (between neighboring brain areas) and long-range connections (between areas of the brain that are further apart). A leading theory of brain connections in autism is that individuals with autism may have under-connectivity in long-range connections, and over-connectivity in short-range connections.

If proven accurate, this could explain some of the behaviors of individuals with autism, including difficulties in complex tasks that require the integration of information from multiple brain regions, but a coequal lack of difficulty, sometimes even enhanced abilities, in tasks that require less integration across different brain areas or regions.

Another possible distinguishing characteristic of brain connectivity in individuals with ASD is that there are too many connections between brain cells. The brain undergoes continual growth and development – especially for young children. Connections are made in the brain every time something new is learned. Over time, the connections that are reinforced become stronger, while connections that aren't reinforced disappear. This is a natural "pruning" process by which room is made for important information and connections, and the rest are "pruned" away as needed.

For children with ASD, however, this pruning process doesn't take place as much as it typically does in other children. It is hypothesized that this might explain the brain overgrowth or the faster growth of the brain of children with ASD during their early years. It might also explain why connections are not as efficient – bad connections are sometimes made, or information could be lost through wrong connections. The brains of babies with ASD have been shown to have more cells than they actually need, including bad connections between cells.

It is believed that synaptic connections between neurons are altered in autism. Either there are too many, too few, too strong, too weak, or wrongly-placed connections. Because of this, it is possible that children with autism could simply be interpreting the world in a different way. The lack of pruning of unused synapses has resulted in an excess of synapses, many of which were damaged and deficient in a normal breakdown pathway called "autophagy" (Greek for "self-eating") – in which synapse connections were broken down. This could possibly be traced to an overactive protein called mTOR.

In light of these findings, one of the potential medication therapies being looked into now, in fact, is a drug that restores normal synaptic pruning by inhibiting mTOR – even after a diagnosis of autism has already been made. This could favorably affect the mTOR/autophagy pathway in individuals with autism.

Underactive Amygdala

It was first discovered by Cambridge researchers that in people with autism and Asperger's Sydrome, the amygdala is underactive when they are trying to decode facial expressions. This has been linked to higher levels of prenatal testosterone during the first trimester, which helps shape brain development by binding to androgen receptors in the brain. The amygdale is one region of the brain that is rich in these receptors. Studies show that higher prenatal testosterone levels lead to superior attention to detail in infants – and concomitant reduced social skills, similar to the basic symptoms of Asperger's Syndrome.

Chapter Five: Symptoms and Diagnosis

Because autism is a complex developmental disorder, the symptoms include a wide range of possible developmental impairments from communication, social interaction, and repetitive behaviors. There may also be sensory differences, differences in any level of intellectual or learning ability, and anything from comprehension or understanding difficulties, impaired social functions, to severe disabilities. These spectrum of impairments can range anywhere from mild or minimal to severe.

Signs and Symptoms

Research has shown that the signs and symptoms of autism are present from a young age, and recognition of these signs and early intervention can result in the best outcomes for children with ASD.

The following are "red flags" that are possible indications of ASD. Should your child show any of the following signs and symptoms, it is highly recommended that you go to a medical specialist for a diagnostic testing. Keep in mind that the presence of a few symptoms does not necessarily mean that your child has ASD. There must be multiple symptoms that disrupt a person's ability to communicate, form relationships, explore, play, and learn.

- No babbling by 12 months

- Delayed speech and language skills

- No back-and-forth gestures such as pointing, showing, reaching, or waving by 12 months

- No big smiles or other warm, joyful expressions by six months or thereafter; flat or inappropriate facial expressions

- No back-and-forth sharing of sounds, smiles or other facial expressions by nine months

- No meaningful, two-word phrases (not including imitating or repeating) by 24 months

- Any loss of speech, babbling, or social skills at any age

- The absence or inconsistent response to the sound of his/her name being called

- "Stimming" behaviors such as flapping, rocking, spinning, head banging, squealing, spinning in circles, constantly feeling textures, or repeating words and phrases

- Inconsistent use of eye contact, gestures (e.g., pointing or shaking one's head), and facial expressions to convey needs and desires

- A showing of limited interest by the child in watching or playing with other children

- Unusual reactions to the sound, smell, taste, look, or feel of things

- Obsessive interests

- Giving unrelated answers to questions, or repeating words and phrases over and over again (echolalia)

- Avoiding eye contact and wanting to be alone

- Difficulty talking about their own feelings, or difficulty understanding other people's feelings

- Becoming upset by minor and major changes

- Interacts with others only to achieve a desired goal

- Does not understand personal and space boundaries, and avoids or resists physical contact

- Does not understand jokes, sarcasm, or teasing, and talks in a flat, robot-like or sing-song voice

- Hyperactivity and impulsivity

- Short attention span

- Temper tantrums, aggression, or causing self-injury

- Lack of, or more, fear than expected

- Unusual eating or sleeping habits

The symptoms of ASD can manifest at any age, despite being a lifelong disorder that starts in early childhood. The fact of it is that some people simply will not manifest any symptoms until later in life, or until after particularly stressful or traumatic life experiences.

Appearance-wise, there is really nothing that will set individuals with ASD apart from others who do not have the condition. The only differences are behavioral – and these symptoms can range from very mild to very severe.

Diagnostic Criteria for ASD

Due to the lack of any specific identification of the cause or definitive physiological criteria of ASD, there is no single test that can diagnose a child or individual for ASD. The Diagnostic and Statistical Manual of Developmental Disorders (DSM-5) prescribes the necessary criteria to evaluate and diagnose Autism and Spectrum Disorder (ASD) and Social Communication Disorder (SCD) through a comprehensive behavioral and developmental assessment. This is the most recent and updated classification system, published in 2013.

Another major diagnostic classification system currently in use is that prescribed by the International Classification of Diseases version 10 (ICD-10), published in 1993.

Either the ICD-10 or the DSM-5 can be used for diagnosis, as long as the classification system actually used is recorded.

ICD-10 Diagnosis

Under ICD-10, autism is defined as a pervasive developmental disorder (PDD), or a group of disorders characterized by:

- The presence of abnormal or impaired development that is manifest before the age of 3 years; and

- Qualitative abnormalities in:

   o Reciprocal social interactions and in patterns of communication; and

   o Restricted, stereotyped, repetitive repertoire of interests and activities

These qualitative abnormalities are pervasive features of the individual's functioning in all situations. A range of other nonspecific problems may also be common, including phobias, sleeping and eating disturbances, temper tantrums, and (self-directed) aggression.

DSM-5 Diagnosis

Under DSM-5, the concept of an autistic spectrum disorder (ASD) is used rather than a pervasive developmental disorder (PDD). One of the basic differences between these two is that the former makes use of the "autism spectrum" rather than types and subtypes Thus, previous subtypes and classifications recognized in DSM-IV are no longer used. DSM-5 also added the following symptoms and diagnostic criteria:

- New clinical signs of stereotypical speech

- Hyperreactivity or Hyporeactivity to sensory input, or interest in sensory aspects of the environment

But the basic diagnostic criteria under DSM-5 are:

- Persistent deficits in social communication and social interaction across multiple contexts; and

- Restricted, repetitive patterns of behavior, interests, or activities.

Diagnosis is generally made based on observed patterns of behavior. It is imperative that diagnosis be made by trained experts or a team of specialists – the diagnosis of ASD can be complicated and is considered a highly specialized area involving multiple evaluations and tests. Some of the specialists you might have to work with include child psychologists, child psychiatrists, speech pathologists, developmental pediatricians, pediatric neurologists, audiologists, physical therapists, and special education teachers.

A comprehensive evaluation is, of course, ideal. Not only will it give you a more accurate diagnosis, doing so will enable you to determine the best type of treatment your child needs, depending on the types and severity of symptoms he or she is experiencing. Some of the tests and evaluations you may expect include:

- Parent interview
- Medical exam
- Hearing test
- A period of observation in a variety of settings
- Lead screening
- Speech and language evaluation
- Cognitive testing
- Adaptive functioning assessment
- Sensory-motor evaluation

Developmental Milestones and Autism

One of the ways by which autism awareness is promoted is by encouraging parents and families to pay close attention to a child's developmental milestones, and the differences a child might manifest that might be indicative of autism. Particularly in the first months and years of a child's life, parents and families are in the best position to make these observations based on daily interaction. Being able to spot the possible signs of autism early on enables parents and doctors to diagnose the condition earlier, thus paving the way for earlier and thus more effective intervention. It is theorized that earlier treatments, particularly those begun during infancy, may actually support the brain's potential to heal.

Below we detail the developmental milestones that most children go through by a certain age, and compare it with possible developmental delays that a child might experience that could be indicative of ASD. At the same time, children with autism might begin manifesting repetitive behaviors such as rocking or self-stimulating by preoccupation with a single object – for instance, choosing to play repetitively with a single toy.

Should the parents notice any of these developmental delays, it is highly recommended that you seek medical help as soon as possible so that the most appropriate early intervention can be availed of as soon as possible, should it be needed. It bears stressing, however, that not all children with autism will struggle in the same areas of development, nor do all developmental delays automatically mean a diagnosis of autism. These are simply warning signs, and when observed, should be a spur to further medical exploration and behavioral assessment by a qualified professional.

1. Two Months

Developmental Milestones	Possible Developmental Delays Indicative of ASD
Smiles at people, shows enjoyment of interaction, responds to people, will cry or fuss when bored	Doesn't smile at people
Turns head toward sounds	Doesn't respond to loud sounds
Can bring hands to mouth and suck on hand or thumb, coos and makes gurgling sounds	Doesn't bring hand to mouth
Tries to look at parent, follow things with eyes and recognizes people at a distance	Doesn't watch things as they move
Can hold head up and begins to push up when lying on tummy	Can't hold head up when pushing up when lying on tummy

2. Four Months

Developmental Milestones	Possible Developmental Delays Indicative of ASD
Interest in exploring the world, watching faces	Might not look with interest at different toys or objects
Smiles spontaneously, especially at people	Doesn't smile at people
Begins to babble, copies sounds he hears, crying on purpose or cries differently for pain, hunger, or tiredness, responds to affection	Doesn't coo or make sounds
Holds head up, pushes up to elbows when lying on belly, can roll over from tummy to back, holds, shakes and swings at dangling toys	Can't hold head steady
Pushes with legs when supported in a standing position; pushes up to elbows when lying on stomach	Doesn't push down with legs when feet are placed on a hard surface

3. Six Months

Developmental Milestones	Possible Developmental Delays Indicative of ASD
Responds to sounds by making sounds, responds to own name, repeated babbling of consonant sounds (ba-ba-ba)	Doesn't respond to sounds around him
Strings vowels together when babbling, and begins to say consonant sounds	Doesn't make vowel sounds
Shows curiosity about things, tries to get things within his reach	Doesn't try to get things that are in reach
Bring things to mouth, looks around at things nearby	Has difficulty bringing things to mouth
Rolls both ways, begins to sit with help	Doesn't roll over in either direction, seems very stiff, with tight muscles
Likes to play with others, makes sounds to show joy and displeasure, laughing and playing simple games	Doesn't laugh or make squealing sounds

like peek-a-boo	

4. Nine Months

Developmental Milestones	Possible Developmental Delays Indicative of ASD
Watches something as it falls, looks for things he sees you hide	Doesn't look where you point
Copies sounds and gestures or others, understands "no," back and forth sharing of sounds, smiles or other facial expressions	Doesn't respond to own name
Stands while holding on to something, pulls to stand	Doesn't bear weight on legs even with support
Sits without support, crawls	Doesn't sit with help
Makes different noises like "mamamama," copies sounds and gestures of others	Doesn't babble
Has favorite toys, plays peek-a-boo	Doesn't play games that involve back-and-forth play

5. One Year

Developmental Milestones	Possible Developmental Delays Indicative of ASD
Will respond when their name is called	Will not yet respond when name is called, and will typically avoid eye contact; will also struggle in interacting or playing with others
Will look at objects when named, and able to follow simple directions	Child could seem like he is in his own world
Sits independently, pulls up to stand, walks holding on to things, can stand alone	Can't stand even when supported
Finds hidden things easily, explores things by shaking, banging, throwing, follows simple directions like "pick up toy," starts to use things correctly	Doesn't search for things that he sees you hide
Looks at things when you name them, pokes with	Doesn't point to things

index finger	
Copies gestures, uses simple gestures, repeats sounds or actions to get attention, shows distress at the loss of toys, anxious at separation from caregivers	Doesn't learn gestures

6. Two Years

Developmental Milestones	Possible Developmental Delays Indicative of ASD
Imitates adult behavior, especially from adults and older children, makes or copies straight lines and circles, repeats words overheard in conversation, displays frustration, pride, affection, and other emotions	Doesn't copy actions and words, repeating sounds, words or phrases over and over again
Follows simple instructions, shows more and more	Doesn't follow simple instructions, self-stimulatory

independence, shows defiant behavior, begins to communicate own needs through single words or gestures, follows two-step instructions such as "pick up your toys and put them in the closet"	behavior with repetitive motor movements like spinning in circles, flapping hands or rocking their body ack and forth
Says sentences with 2-4 words that don't involve imitating or repeating, points to things or pictures when named, knows names of familiar people and things, completes familiar sentences and rhymes	Doesn't use 2-word phrases, might struggle with spontaneous speech and expressions
Plays simple make-believe games, names items in a picture book, points to things in a book, builds towers with 4 or more blocks, might use one hand more than the other, throws ball overhand	Doesn't know what to do with common things like a fork, spoon, phone, lacks imaginative play skills

Stands on tiptoe, kicks a ball, learns to run, climbs up and down furniture without help, walks up and down stairs while holding on	Doesn't walk steadily
Plays with other children, begins to include other children in games, finds things even when hidden under 2-3 covers, sorts shapes and colors, plays simple make-believe games, copies lines or circles when drawing	Begins to display repetitive behavior and/or obsessive-compulsive, non-functional rituals or routines

7. Three Years

Developmental Milestones	Possible Developmental Delays Indicative of ASD
Talks well enough for strangers to understand most of the time	Drools or has very unclear speech
Carries on a conversation	Doesn't speak in sentences

using 2-3 sentences, identifies body parts and colors, uses plural words	
Follows instructions with 2-3 steps, understands most sentences	Doesn't understand simple instructions
Shows a wide range of emotions, may get upset with major changes in routine, copies adults and friends, shows affection, dresses and undresses himself, climbs, runs, walks up and down stairs, pedals a tricycle, running	Doesn't make eye contact
Takes turn in games, shows concern for a crying friend, Understands "his" and "mine," understands gender, plays pretend, watches and interacts with other children	Doesn't want to play with other children or with toys
Pretends to play different characters or talk to dolls or	Doesn't play pretend or make-believe

other toys	
Can play toys with moving parts, puzzles with 3-4 pieces, copies a circle with pencil or crayon, can build tower of more than 6 blocks	Can't work simple toys, Falls down a lot or has trouble with stairs

8. Four Years

Developmental Milestones	Possible Developmental Delays Indicative of ASD
Can say first and last name, sings a song, tells a story or tells a poem from memory	Speaks unclearly
Understands basic rules of grammar, understands "same" and different,"	Doesn't use "you" and "me" correctly, doesn't understand "same" and "different"
Can follow 3-part commands	Doesn't follow 3-part commands
Tells stories, remembers parts of a story, tells you what he thinks is going to	Can't retell a favorite story

happen next in a story	
Can name colors and numbers, understands the idea of counting, starts to understand time, uses scissors, plays board or card games, more creative with make-believe play, engages in fantasy play	Shows no interest in interactive games or make-believe
Plays "mom" and "dad," would rather play with other children than by himself, cooperates with other children, uses more elaborate pretend play routines	Ignores other children, doesn't respond to people outside the family, can name friends when asked

9. Five Years

Developmental Milestones	Possible Developmental Delays Indicative of ASD
Speaks very clearly, tells a simple story using full sentences, speaks in	Doesn't talk about daily activities or experiences

sentences of at least four or five words	
Uses future and past tense	Doesn't use plurals or past tense properly
Wants to please friends, wants to be like friends, shows concern and sympathy for others, has friends	Doesn't show a wide range of emotions
More likely to agree with rules, sometimes demanding and sometimes very cooperative	Shows extreme bad behavior (unusually fearful, aggressive, shy, or sad)
Likes to sing, dance, and act	Unusually withdrawn and not active
Is aware of gender, knows about things used every day, like money and food	Doesn't respond to people, or responds only superficially
Shows more independence	Can't brush teeth, wash and dry hands, or get undressed without help

Co-occurring Conditions and Co-Morbidities

Oftentimes, the presence of ASD in an individual comes with co-occurring conditions or co-morbid disorders which occur at the same time. The significance of recognizing these co-occurring conditions has to do with the possible changes in diagnosis and effective treatment that may be prescribed, based on the individual's specific needs – particularly as they grow older. Many children with ASD do, in fact, have other developmental or other conditions such as learning disabilities, speech delays, attention or seizure disorders, and anxiety. These other conditions may sometimes be treatable with other forms of medication or other behavioral or educational interventions, rather than just treating ASD alone – for instance, ADHD, anxiety disorders, epilepsy depression, and learning disabilities. In this way, treatment of ASD itself may be easier to target.

On the other hand, the presence of co-occurring or co-morbid conditions can sometimes worsen the symptoms of ASD. Making a distinction between ASD and other co-occurring conditions can oftentimes be difficult because many of their symptoms do overlap, making traditional diagnosis difficult. This is why it is so important that a diagnosis be made by an experienced specialist or a panel of specialists. In a very real way, diagnosis paves the way for the treatment, so the more accurate the diagnosis, the more appropriate and, hopefully, the more effective the prescribed treatment.

Some of the co-occurring conditions and disorders that may be diagnosed together with ASD include:

- ADHD
- Anxiety
- Bipolar Disorder
- Bowel Disease
- Developmental Coordination Disorder
- Hearing Impairment
- Down's Syndrome
- Dyslexia
- Dyspraxia
- Epilepsy
- Fetal anti-convulsant syndrome (FACS)
- Fragile X Syndrome
- Gender Dysphoria
- Genetic Disorders
- Hyperlexia
- Immune Disorders

- Intellectual and Learning Disabilities
- Metabolic Defects
- Obsessive-Compulsive Disorder
- Sensory Problems
- Sleep Problems
- Social Communication Disorder
- Tourette Syndrome
- Tuberous Sclerosis
- Visual Impairment

Chapter Six: Treatment, Intervention and Therapies

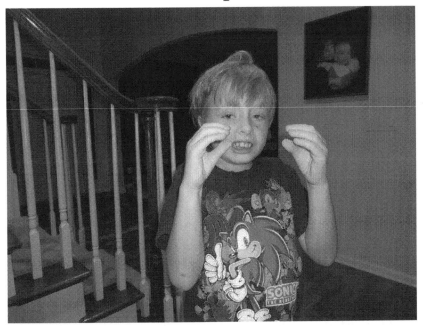

Given the wide variety of symptoms and the differing range of severity, the possible contributory causes, and each individual person's capacity to adjust, there are also several different options for treatment available to people diagnosed with ASD. Each individual is different, and the variety of available treatments, interventions and therapies give people a wide range of available help and support, and thus greater chances of effective help. This is a far cry from the long-ago preferred option of placing people with autism in institutions.

Early intervention is always recommended for children with ASD, which makes early detection and diagnosis also important. Not only will this allow you and your family to adjust early on to the specialized needs needed by your child, but it also allows them to get necessary therapy or help where they might be having developmental delays. Speech therapy for language delays, for instance, can improve a lot with early intervention.

Family participation is particularly important in the multifaceted approach to intervention, treatment and therapy for any child diagnosed with ASD. This gives them a structured environment of possible growth and support right at home, while at the same time providing them with an informed and understanding family with whom learning, communication, and adjustment is possible.

For that matter, the sheer number and variety of treatment and therapy options available to persons with ASD are so varied, with individual responses so different, that families should be fully responsible in educating themselves about the different treatments or programs available and whether or not they think it is appropriate for their child. Most health care professionals will avoid endorsing a specific program or treatment because one cannot really tell what will work for each individual. In the face of so much conflicting information, families should be responsible enough to educate themselves regarding any possible risks or dangers, and make informed choices based on the best interests of the child. Each selected form of treatment should be monitored closely to check for progress. The list provided below, particularly on behavioral interventions and other therapies, are by no means exhaustive.

Medical Treatments

There is no "cure" for ASD, but there are medications that can help a person with ASD function better – for instance, medication to help manage energy levels, or to address conditions such as depression and seizures.

Biomedical treatments have long been in existence for people with autism, but it wasn't until the mid-1990s that these became more accessible to the wider public. This was a direct result of parents and professionals wanting to better understand ASD and how it may be treated effectively.

Medical treatments cover a whole body approach – including specific and individual treatments including dietary changes and vitamin and mineral supplements. Throughout the years, many parents have remarked on the wonderful improvements shown by their children after such treatments.

It is important that families work closely with a trusted medical and health care professional who has experience in treating ASD. The child's progress must be closely monitored, and possible negative side-effects observed. Like most children without ASD, children diagnosed with autism should also have regular medical and dental examinations to keep them healthy, fit and in good condition.

Behavioral Interventions

While medical intervention focuses on the individual's physical health, behavioral interventions in a multi-disciplinary approach are designed to help improve a person's social and emotional health. This is crucial given the difficulties in language, communication, and social interaction experienced by many people with autism. These are designed to provide the child with better structure, direction, and organization to facilitate their continued learning.

Aside from the call to provide better or alternative means of interacting with the people around them, behavioral interventions help by providing a person with autism with the tools by which one can still have meaningful education and thus maximize one's innate potential. With a structured environment that caters to their unique needs, while also addressing their specific symptoms of autism, a multi-disciplinary behavioral intervention approach can help a person with autism live to their full potential, while still enabling them to interact with their environment and communicate effectively with others.

Applied Behavior Analysis (ABA)

APA is one notable treatment that is widely accepted among health care professionals, and is actually being used in many schools and clinics. ABA works by encouraging positive behavior and discouraging negative behavior, while helping the person with ASD to develop and improve a variety of skills.

Some types of ABA include:

- Discrete Trial Training (DTT) – a teaching style that breaks down lessons into simple parts and uses positive reinforcement

- Early Intensive Behavioral Intervention (EIBI) – used for very young children with ASD, younger than five, or three years old

- Pivotal Response Training (PRT) – uses positive changes in behavior to increase a child's motivation to learn

- Verbal Behavior Intervention (VBI) – a focus on teaching verbal skills

Other Therapies

Complementary and alternative therapies like the ones listed below can help by boosting self-esteem, communication skills, or even to reduce some of the behavioral symptoms and sensitivities associated with autism. You might want to check which types of therapies are available to you locally.

- Animal-Assisted Therapies

- Art Therapy

- Auditory Integration

- Cognitive Behavioral Therapy

- "Floortime" or Developmental, Individual Differences, Relationship-Based Approach (DIR)

- Occupational Therapy

- Music Therapy

- Neurofeedback

- Picture Exchange Communication System (PECS)

- Sensory Integration Therapy

- Social Skills Intervention

- Speech Therapy

- Swimming Therapy

- Therapeutic Recreation

- Vision Therapy

Chapter Seven: The Future of Autism Spectrum Disorder

The number of individuals being diagnosed with ASD are growing each year – though it is still not clear whether this is because of an actual growth in numbers, or because of better diagnostic tools and accessibility of resources. In 2013,, it was estimated that autism affects some 21.7 million people worldwide, and in 2010, it was estimated to affect 1-2 people per 1,000 worldwide. In the United States, at least 1 out of every 68 children were diagnosed with ASD as of 2014. And these numbers are only estimated to increase in the coming years.

While there is still much that we do not know about autism, there have already been great strides in diagnosis, research, and available treatments, interventions, therapies, and support networks. People have become more vocal regarding tolerance of those with autism, and worldwide events have promoted awareness of this condition. Educational systems have also adjusted to make room for the special needs of children with autism.

What does the future look for ASD? Hopefully, with increased awareness, diagnoses and intervention can take place earlier, thus providing many children with ASD with crucial support systems that would allow them to make better progress as early as possible. With acceptance and effective treatment options available, numerous individuals with ASD may still be able to live meaningful and fulfilling lives where they can function well in social relationships, family, and even work environments.

Future Directions for Research in ASD

There has already been much progress made in recent years – particularly in our understanding of the pathophysiology of ASD. Of course, the unique challenge regarding ASD is its very broadness of scope requires multidisciplinary approaches – whether it be in the causes, treatments, or diagnosis. The challenge of unifying all the various research information required into a meaningful whole can only be equaled by a concomitant multidisciplinary strategy of different experts in various fields tackling our lack of knowledge about ASD from various angles.

The good news is that a great number of effective tools have already been found, and utilized to good effect, in terms of intervention, treatment and therapy. Many persons diagnosed with autism are now capable of living full lives thanks to crucial developmental skills gained through different therapies, and the growing awareness of autism and greater tolerance to those diagnosed with ASD.

The Necessity of Better Future Planning

Families with children diagnosed with ASD also need to face the reality of their situation – getting crucial help for ASD will cost quite a bit of money. It is estimated that the lifetime cost of raising a child with autism can range from $1.4 to 2.5 million, depending on a child's unique needs. It is recommended that parents and families of persons diagnosed with ASD join groups that can guide them regarding the various details and intricacies of caring for a child with autism, including:

- Guardianship and life insurance policies for the benefit of the child with autism

- Social security and housing and transportation benefits

- Supplemental Security Income or Medicaid

- Financial planning, including trusts, guardianships, and other related issues

- Independent Housing Groups

These are intended to help secure the future of the child with autism, particularly when the parents are gone. As much as possible, making the child as independent as possible is of course ideal.

Long-term Prognosis of People with ASD

It can cause parents a whole load of anxiety when their child is first diagnosed with ASD - from worries about their child's future to worries about how best to provide the care and support their child needs. Thankfully, with better access to treatment, intervention, and support systems, the future of a child with ASD need not look so bleak.

Most ASD-awareness campaigns these days stress "acceptance" rather than "cure." Acceptance is, of course, the first step towards moving forward. The challenges that each child diagnosed with ASD is unique, but not impossible to conquer. In fact, many people with autism these days are actually flourishing – holding regular jobs, living independently, have full and productive lives, and are actively contributing to society. Even for parents, autism is not a condition to be frightened of – it is something to be accepted and understood.

Awareness and education is one of the first steps – thankfully, these days, there are a lot of information and resources regarding how best to cope with the symptoms of autism. There are also plenty of first-person testimonials from autistic people who share some of the things that have helped them overcome difficulties in their lives. The best advice for parents is to read a lot, network, do their research, and at the end of the day, to accept the uniqueness of their child.

Oddly enough, despite how little we actually know about ASD, there is a ton of information out there about it – particularly regarding interventions and treatment options. It is easy for many parents to feel overwhelmed by all this information, and it can be difficult to choose which ones would be most useful to them in their unique circumstances. Networking and joining support groups and connecting with experts, educators, specialists and other families also dealing with autism provides support not only to their autistic child, but also to the families and parents themselves.

Listen, observe, accept, and love your unique child for who he/she is. Most importantly, not giving up is essential.

Index

D

J

L

M

N

O

P

Q

R

Photo References

Page 1 Photo by Linsenhejhej via Wikimedia Commons. <https://commons.wikimedia.org/wiki/File:Autistic_teenage_girl.jpg>

Page 17 Photo by Connie Kasari via Wikimedia Commons. <https://commons.wikimedia.org/wiki/File:Opening_a_window_to_the_autistic_brain.jpg>

Page 31 Photo by nickelbabe via Pixabay. <https://pixabay.com/en/meltdown-autism-autistic-child-1312488/>

Page 37 Photo by Øyvind Holmstad via Wikimedia Commons. <https://commons.wikimedia.org/wiki/File:Gravid_-_pregnant_woman.jpg>

Page 47 Photo by Ralph-Axel Müller via Wikimedia Commons. <https://commons.wikimedia.org/wiki/File:Powell2004Fig1A.jpeg>

Page 55 Photo by nikodem1981 via Pixabay. <https://pixabay.com/en/autistic-education-child-1576873/>

Page 79 Photo by Kfagan6 via Wikimedia Commons. <https://commons.wikimedia.org/wiki/File:Child_with_autism_and_monotropism.jpg>

Page 87 Photo by gpalmisanoadm via Pixabay. <https://pixabay.com/en/groom-father-autism-son-wedding-453953/>

References

"Association Between Maternal Use of Folic Acid Supplements and Risk of Autism Spectrum Disorders in Children." Pål Surén, MD, MPH; Christine Roth, MSc; Michaeline Bresnahan, PhD; et al. <http://jamanetwork.com/journals/jama/fullarticle/157027 9>

"Association of Maternal Diabetes with Autism in Offpsring." Anny H. Xiang, Xinhui Wang, MS, Mayra P. Martinez, MPH, et. al. <http://jamanetwork.com/journals/jama/fullarticle/224714 3>

"Autism." Special Education Guide. <http://www.specialeducationguide.com/disability-profiles/autism/>

"Autism." The National Autistic Society. <http://www.autism.org.uk/about/what-is/asd.aspx>

"Autism." Wikipedia. <https://en.wikipedia.org/wiki/Autism>

"Autism and the Brain." Kimberly Kopko, Ph.D.
<http://www.human.cornell.edu/hd/outreach-
extension/upload/belmonte.pdf>

"Autism Developmental Stages." Autism Love to Know.
<http://autism.lovetoknow.com/diagnosing-
autism/autism-developmental-stages>

"Autism History." News-Medical.net. <http://www.news-
medical.net/health/Autism-History.aspx>

"Autism Myths and Misconceptions." adsd.nv.gov.
<http://adsd.nv.gov/uploadedFiles/adsdnvgov/content/Pr
ograms/Autism/ATAP/Autism%20Myths%20and%20Mis
conceptions.pdf>

"Autism: Signs, Symptoms, and Diagnosis." Total Education
Solutions. <http://www.tesidea.com/autism-signs-
symptoms-and-diagnosis/>

"Autism Spectrum Disorder (ASD)." CDC.
<http://www.cdc.gov/ncbddd/autism/signs.html>

"Autism Spectrum Disorder (ASD) – Treatment." CDC.
<http://www.cdc.gov/ncbddd/autism/treatment.html>

"Autism Spectrum Disorder." Mayo Clinic.
<http://www.mayoclinic.org/diseases-conditions/autism-
spectrum-disorder/basics/definition/con-20021148>

"Autism Spectrum Disorder – Causes." NHS Choices. <http://www.nhs.uk/Conditions/Autistic-spectrum-disorder/Pages/Causes.aspx>

"Autism Spectrum Disorders." HelpGuide.org. <http://www.helpguide.org/articles/autism/autism-spectrum-disorders.htm>

"Autism Spectrum Disorders." WebMD. <http://www.webmd.com/brain/autism/autism-spectrum-disorders#1>

"Autism Symptoms, Causes, Treatment, and More." WebMD. <http://www.webmd.com/brain/autism/mental-health-autism#2-4>

"Autism Symptoms: Early signs of developmental concerns." Dr. Sonya Doherty, ND. <http://treatautism.ca/2013/05/24/autism-symptoms-early-signs-of-developmental-concerns/>

"Autism – Treatment Overview." WebMD. <http://www.webmd.com/brain/autism/autism-treatment-overview>

"Autistic brains develop more slowly than healthy brains, UCLA researchers say." Mark Wheeler. <http://newsroom.ucla.edu/releases/autistic-brains-develop-more-slowly-215407>

"Autistic Spectrum Disorders." Patient Info.
<http://patient.info/doctor/autistic-spectrum-disorders-pro>

"Behavioural Interventions." Autism Canada.
<http://autismcanada.org/living-with-autism/treatments/non-medical/>

"Brain Imaging Research: Structural MRI." Autism Center of Excellence UC San Diego. <https://autism-center.ucsd.edu/what-causes-autism/Pages/brain-research.aspx>

"Brain Study Finds Evidence that Autism Involves Too Many Synapses." Autism Speaks. <https://www.autismspeaks.org/science/science-news/brain-study-finds-evidence-autism-involves-too-many-synapses>

"Breaking into the autistic brain." Parizad Bilimoria. <http://www.childrenshospital.org/news-and-events/research-and-innovation-features/breaking-into-the-autistic-brain>

"Causes." Autism Society. <http://www.autism-society.org/what-is/causes/>

"Causes of Autism." Wikipedia. <https://en.wikipedia.org/wiki/Causes_of_autism>

"Causes of autism spectrum disorder." Raising Children Network. <http://raisingchildren.net.au/articles/autism_spectrum_disorder_causes.html>

"Children with Autism Have Extra Synapses in Brain." Newsroom. <http://newsroom.cumc.columbia.edu/blog/2014/08/21/children-autism-extra-synapses-brain/>

"Conditions comorbid to autism spectrum disorders." Wikipedia. <https://en.wikipedia.org/wiki/Conditions_comorbid_to_autism_spectrum_disorders>

"Congenital Rubella Syndrome." Wikipedia. <https://en.wikipedia.org/wiki/Congenital_rubella_syndrome>

" 'Co-Occurring' Disorders May Explain Change in Autism Diagnosis." Jenifer Goodwin. <http://health.usnews.com/health-news/family-health/brain-and-behavior/articles/2012/01/23/co-occurring-disorders-may-explain-change-in-autism-diagnosis>

"Co-Occurring Conditions or Co-Morbidities." Center for Autism Research.

<https://www.carautismroadmap.org/co-occurring-conditions-or-co-morbidities/>

"Defining Autism." Autism Support of West Shore. <https://www.asws.org/WhatisAutism.aspx>

"Developmental Milestones in Children with Autism." Cara Batema. <http://living.thebump.com/developmental-milestones-children-autism-9766.html>

"Developmental Milestones in Children with Autism." Our Everyday Life. <http://oureverydaylife.com/developmental-milestones-children-autism-5405.html>

"Diagnosis, Causes & Symptoms." Autism Speaks. <https://www.autismspeaks.org/family-services/tool-kits/100-day-kit/diagnosis-causes-symptoms>

"Early Intervention and Autism Terms." Sunny Days, Inc. <http://www.sunnydays.com/glossary>

"Epidemiology." Wikipedia. <https://en.wikipedia.org/wiki/Epidemiology>

"Folic acid." Wikipedia. <https://en.wikipedia.org/wiki/Folic_acid>

"Future Directions for Research in Autism Spectrum Disorders." Cara R. Damiano, Carla A. Mazefsky, Susan

W. White, and Gabriel S. Dichter.
<https://www.ncbi.nlm.nih.gov/pmc/articles/PMC416395
6/>

"Future Planning." Autism Society. <http://www.autism-
society.org/living-with-autism/future-planning/>

"Glossary." Autism Awareness.
<http://www.autismawareness.com.au/could-it-be-
autism/glossary/>

"History of Autism." Project Autism.
<http://projectautism.org/history-of-autism>

"History of Autism." WebMD.
<http://www.webmd.com/brain/autism/history-of-
autism#1>

"Is My Child Autistic? Missed Milestones that Matter."
Alejandra Nathan.
<http://www.themotherco.com/2013/04/is-my-child-
autistic-missed-milestones-that-matter/>

"Medical Treatments." Autism Canada.
<http://autismcanada.org/living-with-
autism/treatments/biomedical/>

"Milestone Checklists." CDC. <http://www.cdc.gov/ncbddd/actearly/pdf/checklists/all_checklists.pdf>

"My child has autism spectrum disorder: what does the future hold?" Raising Children Network. <http://raisingchildren.net.au/articles/autism_spectrum_disorder_prognosis.html>

"Myths." Autism Australia. <http://www.autismawareness.com.au/could-it-be-autism/myths/>

"Myths About Autism." Autism Tennessee. <http://autismtn.org/about-autism/myths/>

"Myths About Autism." Parents. <http://www.parents.com/health/autism/myths-about-autism/>

"Myths About Autism." South Carolina Autism Society. <http://scautism.org/autism-101/myths-about-autism/>

"Navigating Treatments/Interventions/Therapies." Autism Canada. <http://autismcanada.org/living-with-autism/treatments/>

"Other Therapies." Autism Canada. <http://autismcanada.org/living-with-autism/treatments/related/>

"Prenatal SSRI Use and Offspring With Autism Spectrum Disorder or Developmental Delay." Rebecca A. Harrington, Li-Ching Lee, Rosa M. Crum, Andrew W. Zimmerman, Irva Hertz-Picciotto. <http://pediatrics.aappublications.org/content/early/2014/04/09/peds.2013-3406>

"Related Conditions." The National Autistic Society. <http://www.autism.org.uk/about/what-is/related-conditions.aspx>

"Rubella." Wikipedia. <https://en.wikipedia.org/wiki/Rubella>

"The autistic brain." Cambridge Neuroscience. <http://www.neuroscience.cam.ac.uk/research/cameos/AutisticBrain.php>

"The History of Autism." Virgina Sole-Smith. <http://www.parents.com/health/autism/history-of-autism/>

"Therapies and Treatments for Autism." Interactive Autism Network. <https://iancommunity.org/cs/therapies_treatments>

"Treatment Options." Autism Society. <http://www.autism-society.org/living-with-autism/treatment-options/>

"Types of Autism." Research Autism. <http://researchautism.net/autism/types-of-autism>

"Securing the future of a child with autism takes planning, money." Jayne O'Donnell and Laura Ungar, USA Today. <http://www.usatoday.com/story/money/personalfinance/2016/05/11/caring-fo-children-austism-spectrum-cost/83716356/>

"This is What the Future Can Look Like for Kids on the Autism Spectrum." Jamie Pacton. <http://www.parents.com/health/special-needs-now/this-is-what-the-future-can-look-like-for-kids-on-the-autism-spectrum/>

"Understanding Autism – the Basics." WebMD. <http://www.webmd.com/brain/autism/understanding-autism-basics#1>

"What are the Different Names for Autism Spectrum Disorder." Liza Jo Rudy. <https://www.verywell.com/what-are-the-different-types-of-autism-260611>

"What Causes Autism?" My Child Without Limits. <http://www.mychildwithoutlimits.org/understand/autism/what-causes-autism/>

"What causes autism? What we know, don't know, and suspect." Andrew Whitehouse. <https://theconversation.com/what-causes-autism-what-we-know-dont-know-and-suspect-53977>

"What Does the Future Hold for Someone With Autism?" My Child Without Limits. <http://www.mychildwithoutlimits.org/understand/autism/autism-prognosis/>

"What is Autism?" Autism Speaks. <https://www.autismspeaks.org/what-autism>

"What is Autism?" Autism Spectrum Australia. <https://www.autismspectrum.org.au/content/what-autism>

"What is Autism?" MNT. <http://www.medicalnewstoday.com/info/autism>

"What are the causes and is there a 'cure'?" The National Autistic Society. <http://www.autism.org.uk/about/what-is/causes.aspx>

"What Will the Future Look Like for Someone Like My Son with Autism?" Mari-Anne Kehler. <https://www.autismspeaks.org/blog/2014/03/14/what-will-future-look-someone-my-son-autism>

Feeding Baby
Cynthia Cherry
978-1941070000

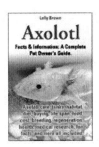

Axolotl
Lolly Brown
978-0989658430

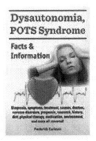

Dysautonomia, POTS
Syndrome
Frederick Earlstein
978-0989658485

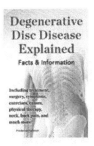

Degenerative Disc
Disease Explained
Frederick Earlstein
978-0989658485

Sinusitis, Hay Fever,
Allergic Rhinitis Explained
Frederick Earlstein
978-1941070024

Wicca
Riley Star
978-1941070130

Zombie Apocalypse
Rex Cutty
978-1941070154

Capybara
Lolly Brown
978-1941070062

Eels As Pets
Lolly Brown
978-1941070167

Scabies and Lice Explained
Frederick Earlstein
978-1941070017

Saltwater Fish As Pets
Lolly Brown
978-0989658461

Torticollis Explained
Frederick Earlstein
978-1941070055

Kennel Cough
Lolly Brown
978-0989658409

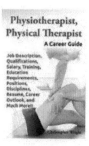

Physiotherapist, Physical
Therapist
Christopher Wright
978-0989658492

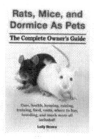

Rats, Mice, and Dormice
As Pets
Lolly Brown
978-1941070079

Wallaby and Wallaroo Care
Lolly Brown
978-1941070031